LITTLE MOOSE, LITTLE MOOSE, PLAYING WITH A GOOSE!

Written by: Chris Roy

DADDY GOT SCARED, BECAUSE HE CARED!

LITTLE MOOSE, LITTLE MOOSE,
PLAYING WITH A GOOSE!

BUMPED INTO A BEAVER,
WHO SEEMED VERY EAGER!

LITTLE MOOSE, LITTLE MOOSE, PLAYING WITH A GOOSE!

MET SOMEONE NEW,
WHO REALLY LIKED TO CHEW!

STOPPED TO OVERHEAR,
ABOUT A SLEEPING GRIZZLY BEAR!

LITTLE MOOSE, LITTLE MOOSE,
PLAYING WITH A GOOSE!

LITTLE MOOSE, LITTLE MOOSE,
PLAYING WITH A GOOSE!

LITTLE MOOSE, LITTLE MOOSE, PLAYING WITH A GOOSE!

SAW A COUGAR NEARBY, AND WANTED TO CRY!

GOOSE GOT CALLED HOME,
AND LEFT MOOSE ALL ALONE!

LITTLE MOOSE, LITTLE MOOSE,
PLAYING BY HIMSELF!

BECAME A LITTLE LONELY,
AND CALLED OUT FOR HIS DADDY!

LITTLE MOOSE, LITTLE MOOSE, ON HIS WAY HOME!

"IT'S MOMMY AND DADDY, WAITING FOR ME!"

UNDER THE CLOSEST MAPLE TREE!

THE END

CPSIA information can be obtained
at www.ICGtesting.com
Printed in the USA
BVHW022144090921
616456BV00002B/11